Robo-Vac

SUSAN GATES

Illustrated by Scoular Anderson

OXFC
UNIVERSITY PRESS

OXFORD

UNIVERSITY PRESS

Great Clarendon Street, Oxford OX2 6DP

Oxford University Press is a department of the University of Oxford.
It furthers the University's objective of excellence in research, scholarship,
and education by publishing worldwide in

Oxford   New York

Auckland   Cape Town   Dar es Salaam   Hong Kong   Karachi
Kuala Lumpur   Madrid   Melbourne   Mexico City   Nairobi
New Delhi   Shanghai   Taipei   Toronto

With offices in

Argentina   Austria   Brazil   Chile   Czech Republic   France   Greece
Guatemala   Hungary   Italy   Japan   Poland   Portugal   Singapore
South Korea   Switzerland   Thailand   Turkey   Ukraine   Vietnam

Oxford is a registered trade mark of Oxford University Press
in the UK and in certain other countries

British Library Cataloguing in Publication Data
Data available

ISBN 978-0-19-911337-8

9 10 8

Available in packs
Stage 9 Pack of 6:
ISBN 978-0-19-911333-0
Stage 9 Class Pack:
ISBN 978-0-19-911334-7
Guided Reading Cards also available:
ISBN 978-0-19-911341-5

Cover artwork by Scoular Anderson

Printed in China by Imago

Paper used in the production of this book is a natural,
recyclable product made from wood grown in sustainable forests.
The manufacturing process conforms to the environmental
regulations of the country of origin.

1

The New Robot

Connor's Great-Gran moved into
a new flat.

'It's made for old people. She's got
lots of machines to help her,' said
Connor's mum. 'Even a little robot to
do the cleaning.'

'A robot?' said Connor. 'Cool!'

He rushed round to Great-Gran's to have a look.

Robo-Vac sat on the kitchen floor. It looked like a silver frisbee.

It had wheels and two arms.
One arm was a grabber, for picking
things up. The other arm was a tube,
as soft and grey as a baby elephant's
trunk. That was for vacuuming. It had
a little brush for a tail.

Connor pressed a button.

Robo-Vac started to hum. It waved
its arms. Its little tail twirled.

Two blue lights, like eyes, lit up on
top of it.

'Aww,' said Connor. 'How cute!'

Then Robo-Vac got busy and started
to clean the kitchen.

It picked up a bag.

It vacuumed.

It brushed and polished.

All the time, it sang a happy little
song.

But Great-Gran wasn't happy.

'I don't like machines,' she said.

'I'm going to send it back.'

As if it had understood, Robo-Vac stopped cleaning. It sat under a table. Its eyes grew dim. It stopped its happy little song.

'It looks so sad,' said Connor. 'You *can't* send it back.'

'*You* have it, then,' said Great-Gran. 'Take it with you.'

'What, me?' said Connor. 'I'm going to play football!'

But the little robot was already humming happily after Connor.

2

'Stop That!'

Connor walked to the park. Robo-Vac
buzzed along behind him, cleaning the
pavement.

'Cool!' said Connor's mates. 'Your
own little robot!'

'Stay there!' Connor told Robo-Vac.
'We're going to play football.'

The game started. At first, Robo-Vac
kept out of the way.

Then, all of a sudden, Robo-Vac
dashed onto the pitch.

It tripped Jason up and started to
clean the football!

'Stop that!' said Connor.

But every time the ball got dirty,
Robo-Vac dashed out to clean it.

'Can't you stop it?' shouted Connor's mates. But the little robot seemed to have a mind of its own.

'You're spoiling our game,' said Connor. 'You're just a big pest!'

As if it understood, Robo-Vac's eyes grew dim again. It stopped singing. It looked really sad.

Connor couldn't be cross with
Robo-Vac. It was only trying to help.

Great-Gran didn't want it. Who
would look after it, if he didn't?

'Come on, Robo-Vac,' sighed
Connor. 'Let's go home.'

Robo-Vac hummed along behind
him, happily vacuuming up the leaves.

3

Robo-Vac Cleans Up

Connor took Robo-Vac up to his bedroom.

It started cleaning the floor.

'Hey!' said Connor. 'I like my bedroom messy!'

But the little robot cleaned up everything – dirty socks, homework and pocket money.

'You are starting to get on my nerves,' grumbled Connor.

He should switch it off. But he couldn't do it.

It was so happy and looked at him with such trusting blue eyes. It couldn't help the way it loved cleaning.

'I'll have to wait until its batteries run down,' Connor sighed. 'But it's driving me mad!'

Suddenly, Connor had a brilliant idea.

He took Robo-Vac to his sister Gemma's bedroom.

Gemma was as tidy as Connor was messy. Nothing in her bedroom was ever out of place. She would get on with Robo-Vac really well.

'Hey, Gemma,' said Connor. 'Do you want your own cleaning robot?'

'Wow!' said Gemma. 'A cleaning robot. What a great idea.'

Connor went back to his own bedroom. At last he'd got rid of Robo-Vac. He threw a few things on the floor. Now he could be as messy as he liked...

4

'Take It Back!'

The next morning, Gemma rushed into
Connor's bedroom. Robo-Vac was
humming behind her.

'Please take it back!' Gemma begged
Connor. 'It's driving me crazy!'

'But you *like* things tidy,' said
Connor.

'That's just the point,' Gemma said.
'There was nothing for it to *do* in my
bedroom. So it sat in a corner and
looked really sad.'

'I know,' sighed Connor.

'So I *untidied* my bedroom,' said
Gemma, 'to make it happy again!'

'You didn't!' said Connor. He couldn't believe it. His tidy big sister had messed up her own bedroom, just to make Robo-Vac happy.

'Please, please, please take it back,' Gemma begged. 'I hate being messy.'

'Well, I *hate* being tidy,' said Connor.

Connor and Gemma stared at each other. Robo-Vac was already busy, picking up Connor's trainers and putting them neatly in pairs.

'We've got to *do* something about Robo-Vac,' said Connor.

'But what?' said Gemma.

5

Robo-Vac
Finds A Friend

'What's that noise?' said Connor.

BBRRRR... a deep, growling sound
was coming from outside.

'It's Dad, mowing the lawn,' said
Gemma.

BBRRRRR...

Robo-Vac stopped cleaning. It went
very quiet and still.

It seemed to be listening.

Then, suddenly, the little robot
whisked out of the bedroom.
It slid down the
stairs.

'Where's it going?'
asked Connor.

Robo-Vac clattered
out into the garden.
'After it!' said Gemma.

Connor and Gemma ran downstairs.
Robo-Vac was sitting on the lawn.

Its blue eyes were sparkling like
stars.

'What's it staring at?' said Gemma.

Dad pushed the mower past. The
little robot's eyes glowed even brighter.

'It's looking at the mower,' said Connor.

BBBRRRR! The mower roared past
again. Robo-Vac's cleaning arms waved
about in excitement.

'I think it's in love,' said Gemma.

Connor let out a hoot of laughter. 'In
love? Don't be so silly!'

'Don't laugh!' said Gemma. 'You'll hurt its feelings.'

Connor looked again. Could Gemma be right?

'If I was Robo-Vac,' said Gemma, 'I might fall in love with that mower. Look how tidy the grass is, now!'

Dad put the big mower back in the
shed. Robo-Vac went in behind them.
Gemma peeped through the window.

'Awww,' said Gemma. 'Just look at
those two. How sweet!'

Connor peeped in. Robo-Vac sat next to the mower. The little robot was gazing at it with adoring eyes.

'We're free at last!' said Connor. 'Now Robo-Vac's in love, it's not interested in cleaning up after us!'

Connor rushed up to his bedroom and threw a few things around.

In *her* bedroom, Gemma was busy tidying her books into neat rows.

Out in the shed, Robo-Vac was cuddling up to the mower.

'How great,' said Connor, stretching out on his bed. 'Everyone's happy.'

About the author

My son Alex gave me the idea for this story. His bedroom is really messy. But he says, 'Don't tidy it, I know where everything is.' Like Connor in the story, he'd love a pet robot. However, just like 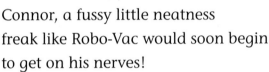 Connor, a fussy little neatness freak like Robo-Vac would soon begin to get on his nerves!